CLAP AND COUNT!
Action Rhymes for the Jewish Year

written and selected by Jacqueline Jules
Illustrated by Sally Springer

KAR-BEN COPIES, INC.   ROCKVILLE, MD

For Arlington-Fairfax Tot Shabbat,
Agudas Achim Gan Shabbat,
and Adas Israel Gan HaYeled...
Your adorable responses were my greatest inspiration.
J.J.

Acknowledgements

"Baking a Hamantash" and "Here's A Yad" by Sara G. Levy from *Mother Goose Rhymes for Jewish Children.* (c) 1960 Bloch Publishing Company, New York, NY. Used by permission.

"When Yom Kippur Begins," by Dorothy Karp Kripke from *Rhymes to Play* © Bloch Publishing Company, New York, NY. Used by permission.

"Five Little Frogs" reprinted with permission from *Fun With Jewish Holiday Rhymes* by Sylvia Rouss. © 1992 UAHC Press, New York, NY.

"In Six Days" by Cheryl Lane; verse by Jonathan Gluck. From *Rosh Hashanah and Yom Kippur: Sing Along with Cheryl Lane and Sean Patrick,* © 1993 Cheryl Lane Music. Used with permission.

"Make A Matzah" by Hyman Reznick from *Jewish Holiday Songs for Children,* recorded by Rachel Buchman. © 1996 Happy Valley Music. All rights reserved. Used by permission.

"The Eight Nights of Hanukkah" by Barbara L. Effron. Used by permission.

"Blue and White Airplane" by Janice Cohen and "Chicken Soup Hot" by Gail Bagdade from *Apples and Honey and Grape Juice, Too! Songs for the Jewish Preschool.* © 1988 by Board of Jewish Education of Metropolitan Chicago. Used by permission.

Library of Congress Cataloging in Publication Data

Jules, Jacqueline
    Clap and Count! Action Rhymes for the Jewish year / Jacqueline Jules; illustrated by Sally Springer.
    p. cm.
    ISBN 1-58013-067-4
    1. Fasts and feasts — Judaism — Juvenile poetry. 2. Jewish religious poetry, American. 3. Children's poetry, American. [1. Fasts and Feasts —Judaism—Poetry. 2. Holidays — Poetry. 3. American poetry—Collections.] I.Springer, Sally, ill. II Title.

PS3560.U5225 C58 2000
811'.54—dc21
                                     00-041214

INTRODUCTION

Rhymes that invite a child's active participation have been popular since ancient times. They help young children to develop coordination and emergent literacy skills. Preschool educators routinely use them to teach counting and basic information about the seasons and holidays.

In this book, parents and teachers will find rhymes about Shabbat, the Jewish holidays, and Jewish traditions. I have included a variety of rhymes for children from infancy to age six. There are knee-and-foot-riding rhymes and tickling rhymes for infants and toddlers. There are finger-and-hand rhymes, face rhymes, clapping, counting, and musical rhymes for preschoolers. Some of them are based on traditional fingerplays such as *Whoops, Johnny, Where's Thumbkin, and Eentsy, Weentsy Spider.* Others are completely original. All of the rhymes were created to promote and enhance Jewish identity in children.

I hope you will have as much fun acting out these rhymes with your children, as I have had with my preschool classes and audiences.

CONTENTS

TWO SHABBAT CANDLES

One Shabbat candle

   Said to her friend,

"It's just about time

For the day to end.

   It's time for the blessing,

   To welcome Shabbat.

  It's time to sing and smile a lot.

Let's stand together,

Straight and tall.

Till our flames burn down

   To nothing at all."

ON FRIDAY NIGHTS

When the big sun in the sky

Drops down, down, down,

Two Shabbat candles

Wear a crown,

A crown of light —

So beautiful and bright —

It sparkles on the ceiling,

Sparkles on the walls,

Sparkles in my heart

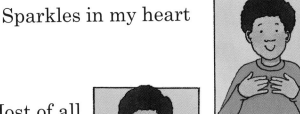

Most of all.

CHICKEN SOUP HOT

Chicken soup hot,

Chicken soup cold.

Chicken soup in the pot

One day old.

Some like it hot,

Some like it cold.

Some like it in the pot

One day old.

SHABBAT SHALOM TO YOU

Candles,   Kiddush,   Challah,   Cake.

Shabbat Shalom!

Shabbat Shalom!

Shabbat Shalom!

To You!

LITTLE SAMMY SPIDER

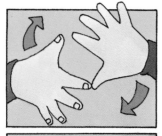

Little Sammy Spider

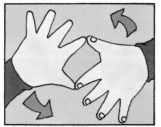

Lived in a Jewish house,

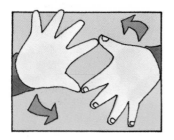

Up on the ceiling,

Quiet as a mouse.

He climbed down his web

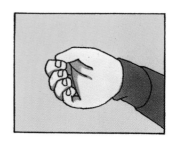

To see the kiddush cup.

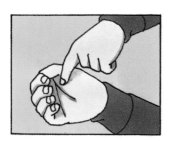

He nearly fell inside,

So he climbed back up.

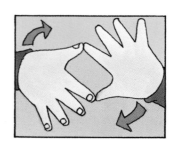

(Tune: Eentsy, Weentsy Spider)

8

IN SIX DAYS

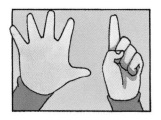 In six days,   la-la-la. (3x)

 God made heaven and earth.

   Then God rested (3x)

 On the seventh day.

   Sun that shines so bright,

Moon and stars at night,

 God created light.

God made heaven and earth.

 Then God rested. (3x)

That's why we have Shabbat.

TEN FRESH CHALLAHS

Ten fresh challahs sitting in a row

Smell so sweet, they tickle your nose.

The baker said,

"I'll wrap one up just for you!

Friday night—bim, bom, true!"

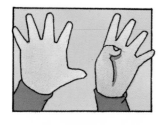

Nine fresh challahs sitting in a row ...

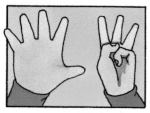

Eight fresh challahs sitting in a row...

Seven fresh challahs sitting in a row ...

Six fresh challahs sitting in a row ...

Five fresh challahs sitting in a row ...

Four fresh challahs sitting in a row ...

Three fresh challahs sitting in a row ...

Two fresh challahs sitting in a row ...

One fresh challah all alone.

The baker said, "I'll wrap it up...

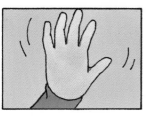

I'm going home. Shabbat Shalom!"

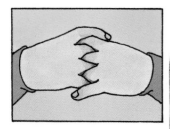

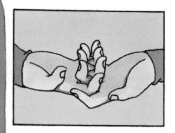

Inside my synagogue

You can see the people pray.

You can see the ark

Where all the Torahs stay.

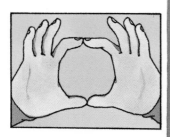

On Shabbat and the holidays

We take the Torahs out.

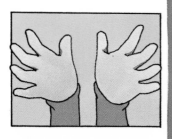

We hold the Torahs proudly

As we march all about.

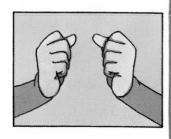

HAVDALAH TIME

 Three stars in the sky

Mark the end of the day.

 Shabbat sadly flies away.

 Watch the shadows in the candlelight,

See the Sabbath soul take flight.

 Try not to frown, try not to weep.

Shabbat joy comes back each week.

THIS LITTLE SHOFAR

This little shofar went toot, toot.

This little shofar went hoot, hoot.

This little shofar made a big sound.

This little shofar was heard downtown.

But this little shofar had something in his throat.

He tried and he tried, but he couldn't blow a note.

So all the other shofars got together,

Tickled their friend with a bright blue feather.

He laughed and laughed till his throat was clear.

Then he wished everyone a Happy New Year!

HONEYBEE

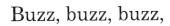

Buzz, buzz, buzz,

Thank you, little bee.

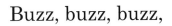

Buzz, buzz, buzz,

For the honey you make me.

Buzz, buzz, buzz,

I dip apples into honey.

Buzz, buzz, buzz,

For a new year sweet and sunny.

Buzz, buzz, buzz.

ROSH HASHANAH ROUND

My challah is round.

My apple is round.

My bowl of honey is round.

I dip apples and challah into honey today,

For sweetness the whole year round.

WHEN YOM KIPPUR BEGINS

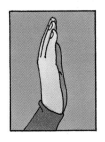 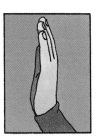

Here's a child,

And here's a child.

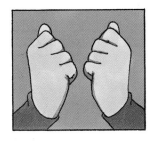

They've quarreled with each other.

When Yom Kippur begins, they must

Make friends with one another.

TWO CHUBBY BABIES

Two chubby babies

Walking through the doorway

Banged heads together on Yom Kippur Day.

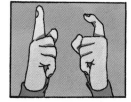 "I'm so very sorry."

"I'm so very sorry."

"Let's take turns going on our way."

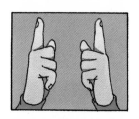

Two thin mommies

Walking through the doorway

Banged heads together on Yom Kippur Day.

"I'm so very sorry."

 "I'm so very sorry."

"Let's take turns going on our way."

Two tall daddies

Walking through the doorway

Banged heads together

on Yom Kippur Day.

"I'm so very sorry."

"I'm so very sorry."

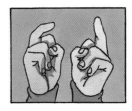

"Let's take turns going on our way."

Two little girls

Walking through the doorway

Banged heads together on Yom Kippur Day.

"I'm so very sorry."

"I'm so very sorry."

"Let's take turns going on our way."

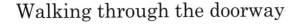

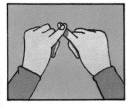

Two little boys

Walking through the doorway

Banged heads together on Yom Kippur Day.

"I'm so very sorry."

"I'm so very sorry."

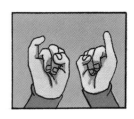

"Let's take turns going on our way."

TWO LITTLE BIRDIES

Two little birdies fly into my sukkah.

They flap their wings and sing, "Tweet, tweet."

On the roof, they see an apple

 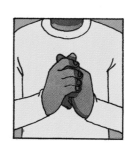

Hanging nicely, ready to eat.

Two little birdies peck, peck, peck —

Soon that apple is nothing but a speck.

SOUP IN THE SUKKAH

I ate lunch in my sukkah today,

My sukkah with branches on top.

I dipped my spoon into my soup,

And I heard a little plop!

I put my spoon on the table,

And I heard another plop!

Then I looked in my bowl,

And plop!

Down came a fat raindrop.

SLEEPING IN THE SUKKAH

Green branches hang above my head

As my bedtime prayers are said.

Three walls protect me from the dark,

And owls that hoot, and dogs that bark.

And when I raise my eyes up high,

I see the stars up in the sky.

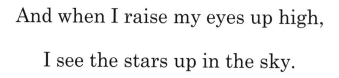

I BUILT A SUKKAH

Bang! Bang! Bang! I built a sukkah.

Bang! Bang! Bang! My sukkah has three walls.

Bang! Bang! Bang! I built a sukkah.

Bang! Bang! Bang! My sukkah's strong, it will not fall.

Bang! Bang! Bang! I built a sukkah.

Bang! Bang! Bang! My sukkah has an open door.

Bang! Bang! Bang! I built a sukkah.

Bang! Bang! Bang! Grass is on my sukkah's floor.

Bang! Bang! Bang! I built a sukkah.

Bang! Bang! Bang! My sukkah has a roof of green.

Bang! Bang! Bang! I built a sukkah.

Bang! Bang! Bang! Through the roof, the sky is seen.

WHERE IS MY FLAG?

Where is my flag?

Where is my flag?

Here it is!

Here it is!

Today is Simchat Torah,

We'll sing and dance the hora.

Let's begin!

Let's begin!

(Tune: Where is Thumbkin?)

We unroll the Torah scroll to read.

The rabbi and the cantor lead.

Every week, all year round,

The Torah is unrolled and wound.

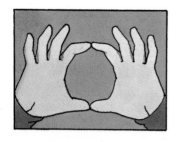

Here is the ark.

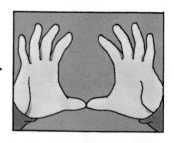

See the doors swing wide.

Where are the Torahs?

Look! It's empty inside.

Look!   Marching in a line.

Up and down   and all around

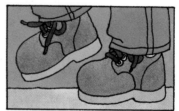

Cause it's Simchat Torah time.

This little dreidel

Spun around in a circle,

Around in a circle,

Around and around.

When will it stop?   Where will it drop?

Wait and watch

Till the dreidel goes plop!

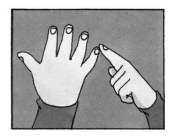

My sister,

She played one.

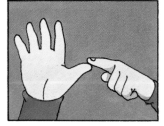

She played dreidel

On her thumb.

With a zig-zag, wig-wag,

Dizzy wizzy spin,

Her dreidel rolled around

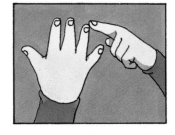

to win.

My brother,

He played two.

He played dreidel

On his shoe.

With a zig-zag, wig-wag,   Dizzy wizzy spin,

His dreidel rolled around to win.

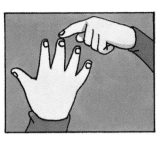

My mommy,

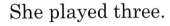

She played three.

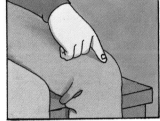

She played dreidel

On her knee.

With a zig-zag, wig-wag,   Dizzy wizzy spin,

Her dreidel rolled around to win.

My daddy,

He played four.

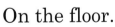

He played dreidel

On the floor.

With a zig-zag, wig-wag,   Dizzy wizzy spin,

His dreidel rolled around to win.

(Tune: This Old Man)

HANUKKAH GELT

One little boy had five pieces of gelt,

And four little boys had none.

The one little boy understood how they felt

And wanted his friends to have fun.

So he said, "Close your eyes

And hold out your hands."

Then he dropped a surprise

 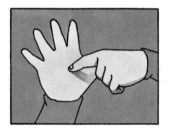 

Into one, two, three, four hands.

Now five little boys unwrap their gelt

 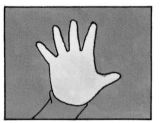 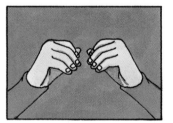 

And gobble it quickly, before it can melt.

EIGHT NIGHTS OF HANUKKAH

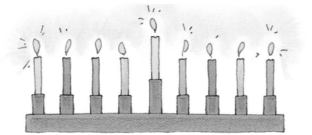

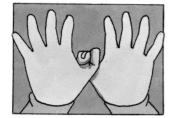

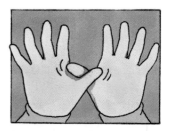

Here is my menorah.

Eight candles in a row,

With the shamash in the middle,

They give a special glow.

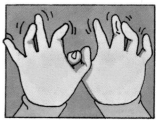

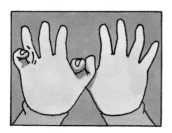

The first candle says, "I'm first in line."

The second candle says, "We shine so fine."

The third candle says, "I'm ready for a treat."

The fourth candle asks for latkes to eat.

The fifth candle wants a dreidel to spin.

The sixth candle hopes to play and win.

The seventh candle sighs at the pretty sight.

The eighth candle recalls the Maccabee fight.

As my candles melt away,

Each one bows down to say,

"It's been fun on Hanukkah

To sing and dance and play."

THE LONELY TREE

Said one lonely little tree,

"Won't you plant a friend for me?"

Said the friend: "Two is nice,

But fun with four, would be twice."

Said the four: "We're not fixed.

To be a group, we need six."

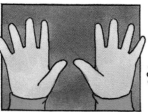 

Said the six, "Trees build our state.

For Eretz Yisrael, we need eight."

Said the eight, "Don't stop at ten, please.

The world needs lots and lots of trees."

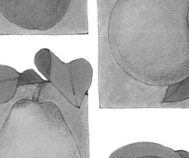

Trees give us shade

When the sun is hot —

One of many reasons

For Tu B'Shevat.

Trees give us fruit —

apple, orange, pear, and peach.

Raise your hand up high and reach.

Grab a juicy and sweet Tu B'Shevat treat.

Ten little trees

Were planted in sand.

They grew up tall

On Israel's land.

Now they sway to the left,

And they sway to the right.

When the wind blows —

Such a pretty sight.

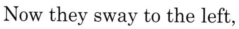

Pat-a-cake, pat-a-cake,

Baker's man,

Bake me a hamantash

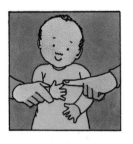

Fast as you can!

Roll it, and fold it,

And make corners three.

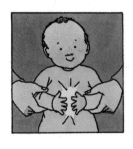

Make one for Mommy,

For Daddy, and me!

Pat-a-cake, pat-a-cake,

Nice baker's man,

Bake me a hamantash

Fast as you can.

SHALACH MANOT

Ding! Dong! Ding Dong!

The doorbell rings all day long.

Purim baskets filled with treats

And hamantaschen good to eat.

WHAT SHAPE IS A HAMANTASCH?

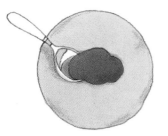

You start with a circle,

Spoon jelly in the middle,

Fold over the corners —

 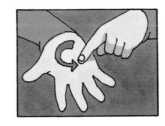 

Now, here's the riddle.

Tell me the shape

Of a hamantaschen cake.

Does it look like a square

When it is baked?

Does it have four sides?

Is it tall?

Is it wide?

If you guessed a triangle which has three sides,

You win the hamantaschen prize.

FIVE LITTLE GROGGERS

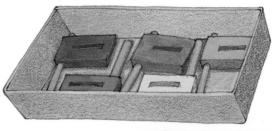

Five little groggers

sat in a box.

They made no sound,

as quiet as socks.

Then the cantor chanted Haman's name.

Clatter, clack, clack, shout!

One little grogger jumped right out.

Four little groggers sat in a box.

They made no sound, as quiet as socks.

Then the cantor chanted Haman's name.

Clatter, clack, clack, shout!

One little grogger jumped right out.

Three little groggers sat in a box.

They made no sound, as quiet as socks.

Then the cantor chanted Haman's name.

Clatter, clack, clack, shout!

One little grogger jumped right out.

Two little groggers sat in a box.

They made no sound, as quiet as socks.

Then the cantor chanted Haman's name.

Clatter, clack, clack, shout!

One little grogger jumped right out.

One little grogger sat in a box.

It made no sound, as quiet as socks.

Then the cantor chanted Haman's name.

Clatter, clack, clack, shout!

The last little grogger jumped right out.

THE HUNGRY PASSOVER MOUSE

This little bitty mouse

Looked for chametz

 All through the house.

 He looked under the sofa,

And under the bed,

 Inside the drawers,

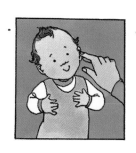

And then shook his head.

"I might as well suck my thumb.

Passover clean means not one crumb."

Chop! Chop! Chop the apples!

Chop! Chop! Chop the nuts!

Mix! Mix! Mix with wine!

My charoset will taste fine!

Light a candle, get a broom, broom, broom.

Search each and every room, room, room.

Tomorrow's Pesach, so we hunt, hunt, hunt

Up and down and back and front, front, front.

Find every crumb you can, can, can.

Sweep the chametz in a pan, pan, pan.

In the morning, we will burn, burn, burn

All the chametz in its turn, turn, turn.

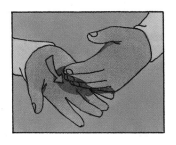

I like to spread my matzah with butter.

I like to hear it crunch.

Sometimes the floor gets messy,

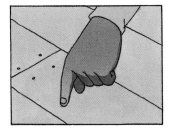

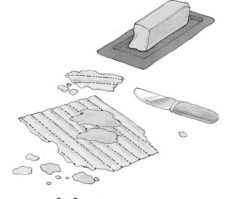

When I eat my lunch.

Mommy gives me a broom and dustpan,

And I sweep up, the best I can.

Make a matzah

Pat! Pat! Pat!

Do not make it   Fat! Fat! Fat!

Make a matzah

Flat! Flat! Flat!

Make a matzah

Just like that!

FIVE LITTLE FROGS

Five little frogs went out one night

And gave the Pharaoh quite a fright.

The first one said,

"I'll jump on his bed."

The second one said,

"I'll jump on his head."

The third one said,

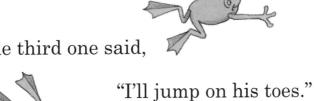
"I'll jump on his toes."

The fourth one said,

"I'll jump on his nose."

The fifth one said,

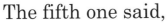
"I'll jump on his face,

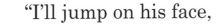

And then we can jump all over the place."

We're going off to Israel,

Riding something with a tail,

Big black wheels,

And silver wings that sail.

It's not a car or bus or train.

It's a shiny silver airplane!

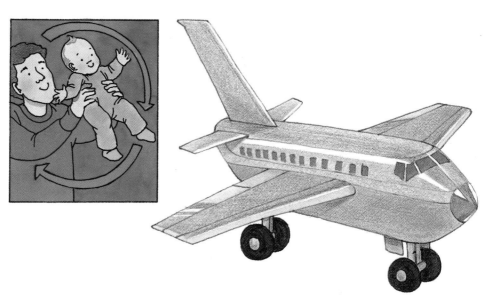

BLUE AND WHITE AIRPLANE

I'm a blue and white airplane

With wings so straight and strong.

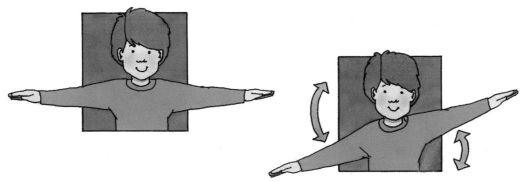

I'm flying to Israel.

Won't you come along?

A CAKE FOR ISRAEL

Today is Israel's birthday!

Guess what we'll make!

Today is Israel's birthday!

Of course, we'll make a cake!

We'll make it two layers tall,

Then frost it blue and white.

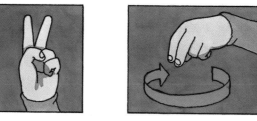

Today is Israel's birthday.

We'll celebrate tonight!

MOUNT SINAI

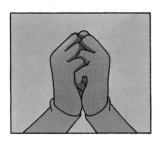

Here is the mountain

That Moses climbed

Way back when

In Bible times.

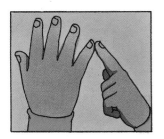

Down the mountain Moses came

With a gift we count and name:

1, 2, 3, 4, 5, 6, 7, 8, 9, 10,

The Ten Commandments,

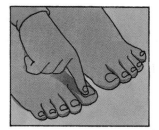

count them again:

1, 2, 3, 4, 5, 6, 7, 8, 9, 10,

Laws to bless our lives. Amen.

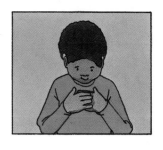

A FLOWER FOR SHAVUOT

I'm a small seed

Planted in the ground.

Watch me gather strength,

As the rains come down.

Ever so slowly,

My leaves uncurl.

I push through the earth

In a graceful swirl.

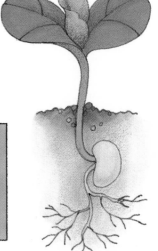

My stem springs up,

And my petals spread out.

Won't I be pretty

When I'm placed all about?

Here's a *Yad*

And here's a *Yad,*

Here are my *Yadayim.*

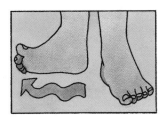
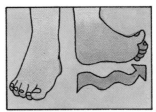
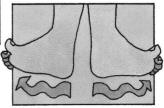

Here's a *Regel,*

Here's a *Regel,*

These are my *Raglayim.*

Here's an *Ozen,*

Here's an *Ozen,*

These are my *Oznayim.*

Here's an *Ayin,*

Here's an *Ayin,*

These are my *Aynayim.*

Tick-tack-toe ...

  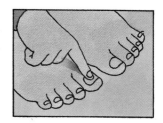

What do you know?

Jews celebrate for lots of reasons.

Holidays come in all four seasons.

Passover comes when the trees turn green then pink.

The flowers bloom, so beautiful you blink.

What time is that? What do you think? *Spring!*

Tick-tack-toe ...

Shavuot comes when the days are long,

The grass is green and the sun is strong.

When do we swim and play ping pong? *Summer!*

Tick-tack-toe ...

Rosh Hashanah, Yom Kippur, Simchat Torah, and Sukkot

Come when the trees have red and yellow coats.

Do you already know or should we vote? *Fall!*

Tick-tack-toe ...

Hanukkah, Tu B'Shevat, and Purim

Come in the season when it snows.

Raise your hand, tell me who knows? *Winter!*

Tick-tack-toe ...

LITTLE ISAAC RABBIT

Little Isaac Rabbit hopping round his bedroom,

Playing with his toys when he's supposed to be in bed.

In comes *Ima* Rabbit — Oh! No! Zoom! Zoom!

Little Isaac Rabbit jumps back into bed.

And *Ima* claps. *"Todah Rabah*!

Thank you very much, Isaac.

Are you ready to say the *Shema*?*"

Little Isaac Rabbit covers his *aynayim*.

He says the *Shema* prayer with *Ima* by his side.

"Lailah Tov!*" Ima* kisses him goodnight.

And shump-bump!

Shuts the bedroom door tight!

(Tune: Little Rabbit Foo Foo)

Do you think Isaac stayed in bed?

Little Isaac Rabbit hopping round his bedroom.

Playing with his toys when he's supposed to be in bed.

In comes *Abba* Rabbit...

In comes *Saba* Rabbit...

In comes *Savta* Rabbit...

Little Isaac Rabbit hopping round his bedroom,

Playing with his toys when he's supposed to be in bed.

Everyone is sleeping—no one opens his room.

When he's finished playing, he jumps into his bed.

Lailah Tov!

GLOSSARY

Abba .... father
Ark .... cabinet where Torah scrolls are kept
Ayin, ayanim .... eye, eyes
Cantor .... one who chants synagogue services
Challah .... braided bread, eaten on Shabbat and holidays
Charoset .... chopped apples and nuts eaten on Passover
Chametz .... bread and other food not eaten on Passover
Dreidel .... spinning top used on Hanukkah
Eretz Yisrael .... the land of Israel
Gelt .... money, chocolate coins eaten on Hanukkah
Grogger .... noisemaker used on Purim
Hamantasch .... three-cornered, filled pastry eaten on Purim
Hanukkah .... holiday celebrating Maccabee victory over Syrians
Havdalah .... ceremony marking the end of Shabbat
Hora .... Israeli folk dance
Ima .... mother
Kiddush .... prayer recited over wine on Shabbat and holidays
Lailah Tov .... good night
Latkes .... potato pancakes eaten on Hanukkah
Maccabee .... Jewish freedom fighter honored on Hanukkah
Matzah .... unleavened bread eaten on Passover
Menorah .... candelabra used to light Hanukkah candles
Ozen, oznayim .... ear, ears
Passover .... holiday commemorating exodus of Jewish slaves from Egypt
Purim .... holiday celebrating the Jewish victory over cruel Haman
Rabbi .... religious leader and teacher
Regel, raglayim .... foot, feet
Rosh Hashanah .... Jewish New Year
Shabbat .... Jewish Sabbath
Shabbat Shalom .... "A peaceful Sabbath"
Saba .... grandfather
Savta .... grandmother
Shalach Manot .... gifts of food exchanged on Purim
Shamash .... helper candle used to light other Hanukkah candles
Shavuot .... holiday commemorating the giving of the Torah at Mt. Sinai
Shema .... central Jewish prayer recited mornings and evenings
Shofar .... ram's horn blown on Rosh Hashanah and Yom Kippur
Simchat Torah .... holiday of rejoicing over the Torah
Todah Rabah .... thank you
Torah .... scroll read in synagogue containing Five Books of Moses
Sukkah .... harvest booth built to celebrate Sukkot
Sukkot .... Festival of Booths, which recalls the Israelites in the desert
Tu B'Shevat .... New Year for the Trees
Yad, yadayim .... hand, hands
Yom Kippur .... Day of Atonement